Moon Adventure

story by Kaye Umansky
illustrated by Steve Smallman

"I want to go to Strange Street again," said Sam.

"Must we?" asked Mouse.

"You push the magic button this time, Mouse," said Ben.

Mouse pushed the button.

"Is this Strange Street?"
asked Jojo.

Strange Street was not the same
as before. The sky was black.
The houses were strange shapes.
The people wore space suits.

"I think we are on the moon!"
said Ben.
"Hooray!" said Mouse. "I like this."

One shop sold space suits.
They were too big,
but Sam wanted to keep her suit on.

"Look!" said Jojo. "I can moon
jump."

Moon jumping was fun!

"Do you want a ride in a moon
buggy?" said a man.

"Yes please!" said Mouse, Sam,
Ben and Jojo. They all got in.

"Push this button," said the man.

The rockets fired.
The buggy went fast!

"Slow down, Mouse!" shouted Ben.

"How?" said Mouse.

"Are you hurt?" asked the buggy man.

"No," said Ben. "But the buggy is."

"Sorry," said the man. "I forgot to show you the stop button. Hop in."

They all got in.

"Where to?" asked the man.

"Back to the lift, please," said Ben.

The man took them to the lift.
"Goodbye," he said. "Safe landing."

WHOOOSH! Home again.

"What a strange adventure,"
said Jojo.